THE UNIVERSITY *of*

C000059034

ANALYSING PRACTICAL SCIENCE ACTIVITIES TO ASSESS AND IMPROVE THEIR EFFECTIVENESS

Robin Millar

The **Association** *for* **Science Education**

Author: Robin Millar

Robin Millar is Professor of Science Education at the University of York. He taught physics and general science in schools in Edinburgh for eight years, before moving to York in 1982. He teaches on the Science PGCE and MA programmes, and supervises at MA and PhD levels. His research interests include the role of science in the curriculum, teaching and learning in science, and the use of diagnostic assessment to clarify and monitor learning goals. He has also played a leading role in several major research and curriculum development projects, including Salters Science, AS Science for Public Understanding and Twenty First Century Science.

Background and context

The analysis framework described in this booklet is based on an instrument originally developed for use in the European *Labwork in Science Education (LSE)* Project in the late 1990s.

This revised framework has been developed to support the *Improving Practical Work in Science* (Getting Practical) programme which The Association for Science Education coordinates on behalf of a consortium of leading science education organisations. Getting Practical is funded by the Department for Children, Schools and Families.

This revised framework forms the basis of the professional development programme offered through Getting Practical. Further information on the programme and sample material from this booklet is available to download on www.gettingpractical.org.uk

Published by The Association for Science Education, College Lane, Hatfield, Herts AL10 9AA

© The Association for Science Education 2010

First printed 2010

ISBN 978 0 86357 425 2

Designed by Colin Barker

Printed by A C Print Solutions

Cover image Science Photo Library

Contents

Introduction

Practical work is a prominent and distinctive feature of science education. Many science teachers and others see practical work carried out by the students themselves[1] as an essential element of good science teaching. As one teacher put it in an interview study (Donnelly, 1995), 'it's what science is all about really ... Science is a practical subject' (p. 97).

Many science teachers believe that student practical work leads to better learning – because we all understand and remember things better if we have done them ourselves. But anyone who has taught science knows from experience that students often do not learn the things we hoped they would learn from a practical activity – and research studies tend to support this view (Millar, 2010). This has led some science educators to question the contribution of practical work to learning. Osborne (1998) argues that practical work 'only has a strictly limited role to play in learning science and that much of it is of little educational value' (p. 156). Hodson (1991) claims that: 'as practised in many countries, it is ill-conceived, confused and unproductive' (p. 176). Perhaps a key phrase here is 'as practised'. Is the kind of practical work we use, and the way we use it, effective in developing students' knowledge, understanding and skills?

It does not seem sensible to ask this question about practical work in general. Practical activities differ considerably in what they ask students to do and what they are trying to teach. If we are interested in the effectiveness of practical work, we really have to consider specific practical activities that we use, or plan to use. The main purpose of this booklet is to provide a tool for doing this in a systematic way – for analysing any given practical activity to clarify its objectives, highlight its main features, and evaluate its effectiveness. Before embarking on this, however, it is useful to explore a littler further what we mean by 'effectiveness'.

[1]Another form of practical work is demonstrations carried out by the teacher with the students observing and perhaps assisting. The focus in this booklet, however, is on practical work carried out by the students.

'Effectiveness' of a practical teaching/learning activity

To think about what we mean by the 'effectiveness' of a practical teaching/learning activity, it is useful to consider the stages involved in developing, carrying out and evaluating such an activity. The model shown in Figure 1 was used in the European *Labwork in Science Education* Project (Millar, Tiberghien, and Le Maréchal, 2002).

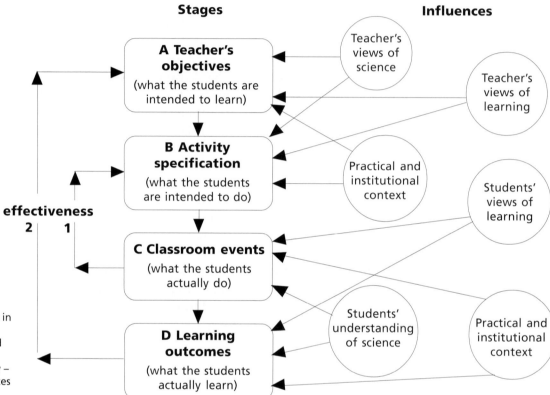

Figure 1 Stages in developing, carrying out and evaluating a practical activity – and the influences on these

The starting point is the learning objectives that the teacher (or whoever developed the activity) had in mind (Box A in Figure 1) – what the students are intended to learn from the activity. These are influenced by several things: the teacher's views of science (e.g. what s/he thinks is important to teach to the group of students in question; his/her ideas about the nature of science and of the enquiry process); the teacher's views of learning (e.g. what s/he thinks is appropriate for learners of the age and stage for which the activity is intended; how s/he thinks learning occurs); and the context in which the activity will be used (e.g. the curriculum or course being followed; how students are assessed; the resources available).

The learning objectives must then be 'translated' into an activity. This might be specified in great detail, or in a less complete and specific manner. The activity specification says what the students should *do* in order to achieve the learning objectives (Box B). It is influenced by the same kinds of considerations as the learning objectives.

When the activity is carried out in the classroom (or in the field), we can observe the events that occur – we can see what the students *actually do* (Box C). This is again influenced by several factors: the students' understanding of science (what they know about the topic in which the activity is set; how competent they are in using the apparatus involved, etc.); the students' views of learning (for example, whether they see their own learning as constructing meaning from experience, or as discovering 'the truth' by observation and measurement, or as being 'given' ideas and insights by a teacher); and the context of the activity (what their curriculum requires; how they will be assessed, the equipment available, etc.). As a result, the actions of the students may be close to what the teacher had in mind, or may differ from it to a greater or lesser extent. It might become clear when we observe a practical activity in action that its design needs to be improved, in order for the students to do what we intended and see what we meant them to see. This is the first, and most basic, sense of effectiveness: the match between what we intended students to do and see, and what they actually do and see. It is about the relationship between Box B and Box C in Figure 1. We might call this 'effectiveness in sense 1'.

Often, however, when people talk about the effectiveness of a teaching activity they mean the extent to which it helped students to learn what we wanted them to learn. This is about the relationship between Box A and Box D in Figure 1. We might call this 'effectiveness in sense 2'.

Two domains of knowledge

The fundamental purpose of much practical work is to help students to make links between two domains: the domain of objects and observables (things we can see and handle) and the domain of ideas (which we cannot observe directly) (Figure 2).

Figure 2 Practical work: Helping students to make links between two domains (Tiberghien, 2000)

In some practical activities, the domain of ideas plays a relatively minor role. For example, we may simply want students to observe an object, or a material, or an event, and notice and remember some things about it. In other practical activities, however, we want students to develop their understanding of specific scientific ideas that are relevant for describing or explaining the observations made. In these activities, thinking is at least as important as doing and seeing; students learn only when the activity is not only 'hands on' but also 'minds on'. To assess the effectiveness of activities of this sort, we need to think about both domains of Figure 2. In the language of the model of effectiveness set out in Figure 1, we need to look at what students 'do' with ideas, as well as what they do with objects and materials (Box C); and we need to look at how well the activity supports their learning of ideas and not merely their ability to recall observable events (Box D).

Table 1 sets this out in more detail. It identifies the kind of evidence that would indicate that a practical activity was effective in each of the senses identified above, in each of the two domains.

A practical activity is:	in the domain of objects and observables	in the domain of ideas
effective in sense 1 'doing'	Students do what was intended with the objects and materials provided, and observe what they were meant to observe	During the activity, students think about what they are doing and observing, using the ideas intended, or implicit in the activity
effective in sense 2 'learning'	Students can later recall and describe what they did in the activity and what they observed	Students can later discuss the activity using the ideas it was aiming to develop, or which were implicit in it (and can perhaps show understanding of these ideas in other contexts)

Table 1 Evidence that would indicate 'effectiveness' in each sense, and in each domain

Practical activities that strongly involve the domain of ideas have a significantly higher learning demand (Leach and Scott, 1995) than those which simply aim to allow students to see and remember an observable event. In such activities, students are likely to require assistance to use or develop the ideas that make sense of the activity, and lead to learning. Activities that have this kind of 'scaffolding' built into their design are likely to be more effective than ones which do not.

As regards 'effectiveness in sense 2' in the domain of ideas (Table 1), we should also be realistic about what to expect. It would be unreasonable to expect durable long-term learning of a scientific idea or concept to result from a single, relatively brief, practical activity. Learning, where it occurs, is likely to result from a sequence of lessons that involve activities of various kinds, including some carefully planned practical activities at appropriate points. Also, the learning of conceptual ideas is rarely an event that occurs at a single moment, and is then irreversible. Most students move in a less linear and less predictable way from their previous ideas towards the scientific ideas we would like them to understand and be able to use. All of this makes it difficult to measure effectiveness in sense 2. Nonetheless we should keep in mind that the purpose of many practical activities is to help students improve their understanding of scientific ideas and explanations, and not simply to increase their factual knowledge of the natural world – and so we need to think about how we might design and present practical activities that have a better chance of supporting this learning.

Analysing practical activities

The previous section made three key points.

- Practical activities are very diverse, so we should consider the effectiveness of practical activities individually, rather than of practical work in general.
- The starting point in considering any practical activity is its learning objective(s).
- The way a practical activity is designed and presented may have a significant influence on the extent to which its learning objective(s) is/are attained.

This section will present and explain an instrument (a checklist) for analysing practical activities to provide a clear description of their principal features. This then provides a basis for considering the effectiveness of a practical activity, and for thinking about how it might be modified to improve its effectiveness. The components of the checklist are shown in Table 2.

1	**Learning objective (intended learning outcome)** - Developing knowledge and understanding of the natural world - Using scientific equipment or following standard procedures - Developing understanding of the scientific approach to enquiry
2	**Design** 2.1 Degree of direction given 2.2 Logical structure 2.3 Importance of scientific ideas 2.4 What students have to do with objects and materials 2.5 What students have to 'do' with ideas
3	**Presentation** 3.1 Students' awareness of purpose of activity 3.2 Explanation of task to students 3.3 Nature of discussion before activity 3.4 Nature of discussion after activity 3.5 Students' record of the activity

Table 2
Components of the practical activity analysis checklist

The complete checklist is shown in Appendix 1. The rest of this booklet discusses each of its components in turn, with the aim of clarifying the coding categories suggested and explaining some of the reasons behind them.

Learning objective (or intended learning outcome)

As regards their learning objective(s), practical activities can be divided into three broad groups that help students:

A develop their knowledge and understanding of the natural world
B learn how use a piece of scientific equipment or follow a standard practical procedure
C develop their understanding of the scientific approach to enquiry

We can then subdivide each of these further, to identify the learning objective(s) more precisely.

Figure 3 suggests a way of doing this. To complete the tables in Figure 3, you first tick one of the three boxes in column 2, to identify the main objective in general terms (A, B or C above). Then you tick one box in the right-hand column to indicate more specifically what students are expected to learn from the activity. If you choose general objective C, and tick the lower box in the right-hand column, you can then provide more detail by ticking the boxes that apply in the table at the bottom of Figure 3.

Of course, some practical activities may appear to have objectives in more than one of the groups A, B and C above. But often one of these is the principal objective – and it can be useful to recognise this. But if you genuinely believe that there are important objectives in more than one of the main groups, an alternative way of using Figure 3 is to enter numbers 1, 2 (and if absolutely essential 3) in the second column, to indicate the priority order of main objectives – and then to tick more than one box in the right-hand column to indicate the specific objective in each of the main groups you have indicated.

Figure 3
Identifying the learning objective (or objectives) of a practical activity

Objective (in general terms)	Tick ✔ **one** box to indicate the main objective	Learning objective (more specifically)	Tick ✔ **one** box
A By doing this activity, students should develop their knowledge and understanding of the natural world		Students can recall an observable feature of an object, or material, or event	
		Students can recall a 'pattern' in observations (e.g. a similarity, difference, trend, relationship)	
		Students can demonstrate understanding of a scientific idea, or concept, or explanation, or model, or theory	
B By doing this activity, students should learn how to use a piece of laboratory equipment or follow a standard practical procedure		Students can use a piece of equipment, or follow a practical procedure, that they have not previously met	
		Students are better at using a piece of equipment, or following a practical procedure, that they have previously met	
C By doing this activity, students should develop their understanding of the scientific approach to enquiry		Students have a better *general understanding* of scientific enquiry	
		Students have a better *understanding of some specific aspects* of scientific enquiry	

If you have ticked this box, please complete the table below

Specific aspects of scientific enquiry	Tick ✔ **all** that apply
How to identify a good investigation question	
How to plan a strategy for collecting data to address a question	
How to choose equipment for an investigation	
How to present data clearly	
How to analyse data to reveal or display patterns	
How to draw and present conclusions based on evidence	
How to assess how confident you can be that a conclusion is correct	

The categories in Figure 3 are influenced by research. Many studies suggest that practical activities whose main aim is A (to help students develop their knowledge and understanding of the natural world) vary considerably in learning demand. If the objective is for students to observe an object, or material, or event that they have not seen before, or not looked at closely before – and to remember what they see – then the learning demand is relatively low. Many students will recall it for some time; the more surprising or striking the observation is, the longer they are likely to remember it. But if the objective is to help students develop their understanding of explanatory ideas, concepts, models or theories, then the learning demand is much greater. Much practical work is relatively ineffective because teachers underestimate the challenge the students face in making sense of what they see. The idea that explanations 'emerge' from observations has been called 'the fallacy of induction' (Driver, 1983). We might expect that activities of high learning demand would be designed or presented in class in ways that reflected this; a recent study, however, found little difference in the way activities of higher and lower learning demand were designed or presented (Abrahams and Millar, 2008).

The way teachers use practical activities whose main aim is C (to help students develop their understanding of scientific enquiry) often seems to imply a belief that 'practice makes perfect' – that students will get better at planning and conducting their own investigations simply through practice. Research, however, tends to suggest that more effective learning occurs when specific aspects of scientific enquiry are identified and taught (Watson, Wood-Robinson, and Nicolaou, 2006; Millar, in press). So the coding scheme in Figure 3 for type C activities aims to encourage you to think in more detail about *exactly* what you want your students to learn from any practical activity of this sort that you use. Some activities with more specific and targeted learning objectives might be more effective – and may help students develop knowledge that they could then apply in other investigative work.

Design of practical activities

Open or closed: Degree of direction given

A frequent criticism of practical work in school science is over-reliance on 'cookbook' or 'recipe following' tasks – where students are given detailed instructions on what to do, often in the form of a worksheet. Students, when doing such activities, often lose sight of the overall purpose of the activity and follow the instructions rather mechanically and without much thought.

To think about this, you might ask, for a given practical activity, how each of the following aspects of the activity is decided upon:
- the question to be addressed
- the equipment to be used
- the procedure to be followed
- the methods of handling data collected
- the interpretation of results

Is it determined completely by the teacher, perhaps via a written worksheet or detailed oral instructions? Or is it, at the other extreme, left entirely open to the students to decide? Or is it somewhere in the middle, perhaps decided after some whole-class discussion about ideas and options, or where the teacher provides a general framework but leaves some choices open to the students? Table 3 can be used to indicate how open or closed the activity is.

Degree of direction given (how open/closed?)	Tick ✔ **one** box
Question given, and detailed instructions on procedure	
Question given, and outline guidance on procedure; some choices left to students	
Question given, but students choose how to proceed	
Students decide the question and how to proceed	

Table 3 Degree of direction given (how open/closed?)

Logical structure

Another important aspect of a practical activity is the extent to which it is 'data driven' or 'ideas driven'. Does the activity begin by collecting data in the form of observations and measurements 'to see what happens'? Or does it start from thinking about a situation or question, perhaps saying what we might expect, and then collecting data to see if this is correct or has to be modified? Tasks with this second kind of logical structure are more likely to integrate thinking and doing. Also, as discussed earlier, there is a risk that activities that begin from data may be based on what Driver (1983) called 'the fallacy of induction', that is, the idea that explanations 'emerge' from observations. This significantly underestimates the challenge for learners. An explanation may be obvious to the teacher, who already knows it, but not at all obvious to a student. If much practical work is ineffective for developing students' understanding of ideas and explanations, as research seems to suggest, then part of the reason may lie in the logical structure of the practical activities we use. So it is useful to reflect on this aspect of design – particularly for activities that aim to develop understanding of explanatory ideas.

Some activities may not, of course, fall neatly into either of the two categories described, so a third option is provided in Table 4.

Table 4 Logical structure of a practical activity – data driven or ideas driven?

Logical structure	Tick ✔ **one** box
Collect data on a situation, then think about how it might be summarised or explained	
Use current ideas to generate a question or prediction; collect data to explore or test	
Other: describe briefly:	

Importance of an understanding of scientific ideas

Some practical activities can be carried out without much scientific knowledge about the task or its context. Others really only make sense if you have some scientific understanding. And interpreting what you observe can make small or large demands on your scientific understanding. It is worth reflecting on how important it is to have some understanding of scientific ideas in order to carry out an activity well.

For activities whose general objective is 'A: to help students develop their knowledge and understanding of the natural world', those with the more specific objective that 'Students can demonstrate understanding of a scientific idea, or concept, or explanation, or model, or theory' are appreciably more demanding than those where we simply want students to be able to recall an observable event, or a simple pattern in observations.

Also, for activities whose general objective is 'C: to help students develop their understanding of the scientific approach to enquiry', the learning demand may be significantly higher if the practical activity requires an understanding of scientific ideas and explanations than if it is based on everyday ideas and principles.

Even for activities with general objective 'B: to help students learn how to use a piece of laboratory equipment or follow a standard practical procedure', the level of difficulty may be higher if understanding how the equipment or the procedure works is important for using, or following, it. It is therefore useful to ask, for any practical activity, how important an understanding of scientific ideas is, in order to carry out the activity well. A convenient way to do this is to rate the activity on a four-point scale: 4 = essential; 3 = fairly important; 2 = not very important; 1 = unimportant.

What students have to do with objects and materials

Practical activities require students to *do things* with objects and materials. Indeed this might be regarded as the defining characteristic of 'practical work'. But the things students are expected to do can be quite diverse. Table 5 suggests a way of describing what a given activity requires students to do with objects and materials. Although all are written in the singular, they should be read as either singular or plural (e.g. the final option also includes activities where students have to measure several quantities, not just 'a quantity').

These categories are not mutually exclusive; you might need to tick several. For example, if an activity is simply intended to teach students how to use an instrument or follow a procedure, then you might only tick option 1 or 2. But if students have to measure a quantity (option 8), they are likely also to have to 'use a scientific instrument'. 'Present or display an object or material' (option 3) includes activities such as a dissection, or presenting a set of rock samples to show the main types. Many tasks require students to make something, for example, a model d.c. motor (an object – option 4), or a sample of hydrogen (a substance – option 5), or to 'produce a phenomenon' (option 6) (for example, refraction through a glass block, or a positive starch test on a leaf sample).

	What students have to do with objects and materials	Tick ✔ all that apply
1	Use a scientific instrument	
2	Follow a standard practical procedure	
3	Present or display an object or material	
4	Make an object	
5	Make a sample of a material or substance	
6	Make an event happen (produce a phenomenon)	
7	Observe an aspect or property of an object, material, or event	
8	Measure a quantity	

Table 5 What students have to do with objects and materials, in a given practical activity

What students have to 'do' with ideas

Practical activities require students to 'do' things not only with objects and materials, but also with ideas. Table 6 suggests way of describing this aspect of a given practical activity.

	What students have to do with ideas	Tick ✔ all that apply
1	Report observations using scientific terminology	
2	Identify a similarity or difference (between objects, or materials, or events)	
3	Explore the effect on an outcome of a specific change (e.g. of using a different object, or material, or procedure)	
4	Explore how an outcome variable changes with time	
5	Explore how an outcome variable changes when the value of a continuous input variable changes	
6	Explore how an outcome variable changes when each of two (or more) input variables changes	
7	Design a measurement or observation procedure	
8	Obtain a value of a derived quantity (i.e. one that cannot be directly measured)	
9	Make and/or test a prediction	
10	Decide if a given explanation applies to the particular situation observed	
11	Decide which of two (or more) given explanations best fits the data	
12	Suggest a possible explanation for data	

Table 6 What students have to do with ideas, in a given practical activity

If possible, you should try to tick just one category that best describes the 'thinking' aspect of the activity. But, you may feel you have to tick more than one to describe an activity adequately.

If the focus of an activity is on enabling students to see an unfamiliar phenomenon, then all they may be required to do that involves ideas is to talk (or write) about what they have done using some scientific terms (option 1). In some activities (option 2), the task is to identify a pattern of similarity or difference, e.g. to notice that the flame colour is the same when salts of the same metal are burned. This involves making an inference from the data collected.

Options 3 to 6 describe different types of 'relationships between variables' tasks. The terms 'input' and 'outcome' variable are used in preference to 'independent' and 'dependent' variable – which many students have difficulty with.

In some activities (option 7), the largest cognitive challenge is to think of a way to measure or observe the thing you are interested in, for example, measuring the volume of gas produced when a measured amount of a carbonate reacts with a quantity of dilute acid. 'Obtain[ing] a value of a derived quantity' (option 8) means measuring a variable such as density or speed that requires you to measure some other primary quantities and do a calculation.

Finally, options 9 to 12 apply to activities in which explanations are important. These activities are more likely to be 'minds on' than those where the emphasis is only on objects, materials and observable properties. For example, if it is possible to redesign an activity to give it a Predict-Observe-Explain (POE) structure (White and Gunstone, 1992), this can significantly enhance student engagement and learning.

Presentation of practical activities

The design features of a practical activity could be coded from written (or oral) instructions on the activity. But other aspects of a practical activity could only be described and coded by a person who has used it, or plans to use it, or by someone who has observed it being used. These aspects concern the way the activity is presented to students.

Any given practical activity can be presented in a variety of ways. Important components of presentation are: how students understand the purpose of the activity, how it is explained to them, what discussion precedes or follows it, and how it is recorded. The way a practical activity is presented can have a significant effect on its effectiveness in learning terms.

Students' awareness of the purpose of a practical activity

One aspect of the presentation of an activity to students is their awareness of its purpose: can they see *why* they are doing it? On the basis of their *current understanding*, can they grasp what it is about? Is it a way of answering a question they are already thinking about, or of exploring an issue they have become interested in – or is it just 'what the teacher has told us to do today'? Table 7 suggests some categories for summarising this for a given practical activity.

Table 7
Students' awareness of the purpose of a given practical activity

Students' awareness of purpose of activity	Tick ✔ **one** box
Activity is proposed by teacher; no explicit links made to previous work	
Purpose of activity explained by teacher, and explicitly linked to preceding work	
Teacher uses class discussion to help students see how the activity can help answer a question of interest	
Purpose of activity readily apparent to the students; clearly follows from previous work	
Activity is proposed and specified by the students, following discussion	

Explanation of the practical activity to students

Teachers use a range of methods of outlining and explaining a practical activity to students. Oral instructions might be given, perhaps supported by written instructions or diagrams on a board, or displayed on a screen. Another common practice is to issue a worksheet. Sometimes teachers may demonstrate aspects of the equipment or the procedures to be followed, before the students start work themselves. Table 8 summarises these possibilities.

How students are told what they have to do in the practical activity	Tick ✔ all that apply
Orally by the teacher	
Written instructions on OHP or data projector	
Worksheet	
(All or part of) procedure demonstrated by teacher beforehand	

Table 8 How the practical activity is explained to students

Nature of discussion before and after the practical activity

The discussion that precedes a practical activity is critical in helping students see the purpose of the activity and appreciate how it might help them develop their knowledge or skills. Many science educators have also argued that most of the learning that results from a practical activity arises from the discussion that follows it. This is particularly so if the activity aims to develop students' understanding of a scientific idea, or concept, or explanation, or model, or theory. So the nature of the discussion before and after the practical activity is important.

Tables 9 and 10 suggest some categories that may be useful for this. In both cases, more than one may apply, so you may need to tick more than one box. A recent research study (Abrahams and Millar, 2008) found that most of the talk before practical activities was about the equipment and procedures to be used, and very little (often none) was about the ideas needed to make sense of the activity or interpret the data. The same study also found that there was almost no discussion, during or after practical activities, about the investigation design, the quality of the data collected, or the confidence we might have in the conclusions drawn – even where there were clear opportunities to draw out and explore ideas about scientific enquiry.

The coding categories in Tables 9 and 10 draw attention to the need to consider the use, and the focus, of pre-task and post-task discussion. Making changes here could significantly enhance learning effectiveness. Abrahams and Millar (2008) also noted several instances of option 3 in Table 10: repeating an entire practical activity as a teacher demonstration after students have done it themselves. This seems a very risky strategy if it is used regularly – as students may come to expect that it will happen and hence be less concerned to carry out their own practical work carefully or to think about how their data might be explained.

Nature of discussion *before* practical activity	Tick ✔ all that apply
None	
About equipment and procedures to be used	
About ideas, concepts, theories, and models that are relevant to the activity	
About aspects of scientific enquiry that relate to the activity	

Table 9 Class discussion *before* the practical activity

Nature of discussion *after* the practical activity	Tick ✔ all that apply
None	
About confirming 'what we have seen'	
Centred around a demonstration in which the teacher repeats the practical activity	
About how to explain observations, and to develop conceptual ideas that relate to the task	
About aspects of investigation design, quality of data, confidence in conclusions, etc.	

Table 10 Class discussion after the practical activity

Students' record of the activity

A final aspect of presentation concerns the record that students make and keep of the practical activity (Table 11). The practice followed might reflect the purpose of this record. Is 'writing up' seen as part of the process of coming to an understanding of ideas, or is it largely to record ideas that have been understood? Do students keep a written record as evidence of what they have done, or as a basis for revision for a later summative test? Or is the purpose to help students develop the skills associated with writing a scientific report? Table 11 lists the most common options, but also includes space to summarise briefly any other form of record keeping used. As with several other aspects of design and presentation discussed above, it might be more interesting and valuable to audit the variety of practice over a term or a school year in this aspect of practical work, than simply to code individual practical activities.

Table 11 Students' record of the activity

Students' record of the activity	Tick ✔ **one** box
None	
Notes, as the student wishes	
A completed worksheet	
Written report with a given format	
Written report in a format chosen by the student	
Other. Please describe:	

Using this analysis checklist

The purpose of the analysis checklist described above is to enable a teacher, or a researcher, to audit practical activities that are currently used, or being considered for use, in a systematic way. The coding categories have been chosen in the light of the science education literature on practical work – to highlight issues that science educators have thought important, and draw attention to key issues and choices.

The whole checklist is shown in Appendix 1. The second page ends with a section headed 'Learning demand'. The discussion above has highlighted some of the features of a task that might increase or lower its learning demand – the size of the cognitive challenge it presents to the students (Leach and Scott, 1995). After coding an activity in terms of its learning objective(s), its design and its presentation, it is useful to make an overall assessment of its learning demand on a 5-point scale from 'very high' to 'very low'. The third and final page of the checklist then consists of tables that can be used, after a practical activity has been implemented, to review its effectiveness in the two senses (doing and learning) discussed in 'Effectiveness of a practical teaching/learning activity' in this booklet.

An alternative version allowing coding of 10 practical activities is included as Appendix 2. This could be used to analyse practical activities used in the teaching of a science topic, or during a specific period of time – in order to get a picture of the variety of practice and learning demand, so that this can be considered and reviewed.

A final word

The practical activity analysis checklist described in this booklet is intended to be a useful tool, not a restrictive straitjacket. If you use it, you may find that you want to add new components of design or presentation, or new categories for describing some of these components. If so, you should do so. The value of an instrument of this sort lies mainly in the thinking that it can stimulate about practical activities, their objectives, design and presentation.

References

Abrahams, I., and Millar, R. (2008). Does practical work really work? A study of the effectiveness of practical work as a teaching and learning method in school science. *International Journal of Science Education*, 30 (14), 1945-1969.

Donnelly, J. (1995). Curriculum development in science: The lessons of Sc1. *School Science Review*, 76 (277), 95-103.

Driver, R. (1983). *The pupil as scientist?* Chapter 1. The fallacy of induction in science teaching (pp. 1-10). Milton Keynes: Open University Press.

Hodson, D. (1991). Practical work in science: Time for a reappraisal. *Studies in Science Education*, 19, 175-184.

Leach, J., and Scott, P. (1995). The demands of learning science concepts: Issues of theory and practice. *School Science Review*, 76 (277), 47-52.

Millar, R. (2010). Practical work. In J. Dillon and J. Osborne (Eds.), *Good practice in science teaching: What research has to say*, 2nd edn. London: McGraw-Hill.

Millar, R., Tiberghien, A., and Le Maréchal, J.-F. (2002). Varieties of labwork: A way of profiling labwork tasks. In D. Psillos and H. Niedderer (Eds.), *Teaching and learning in the science laboratory* (pp. 9-20). Dordrecht: Kluwer Academic Publishers.

Osborne, J. (1998). Science education without a laboratory? In J.J. Wellington (Ed.), *Practical work in school science. Which way now?* (pp. 156-173). London: Routledge.

Tiberghien, A. (2000). Designing teaching situations in the secondary school. In R. Millar, J. Leach, and J. Osborne (Eds.), *Improving science education: The contribution of research* (pp. 27-47). Buckingham: Open University Press.

Watson, R., Wood-Robinson, V., and Nikolaou, L. (2006). Better scientific enquiries. In V. Wood-Robinson (Ed.), *ASE guide to secondary science education* (pp. 196-204). Hatfield: Association for Science Education.

White, R., and Gunstone, R. (1992). *Probing understanding.* Chapter 3. Prediction – Observation – Explanation (pp. 44-64). London: Falmer Press.

A checklist for analysing and evaluating a single practical activity

Title:	

1 Learning objective(s) (or intended learning outcome(s))

Objective (in general terms)	Tick ✔ one box to indicate the main objective	Learning objective (more specifically)	Tick ✔ one box
A By doing this activity, students should develop their knowledge and understanding of the natural world		Students can recall an observable feature of an object, or material, or event	
		Students can recall a 'pattern' in observations (e.g. a similarity, difference, trend, relationship)	
		Students have a better understanding of a scientific idea, or concept, or explanation, or model, or theory	
B By doing this activity, students should learn how to use a piece of laboratory equipment or follow a standard practical procedure		Students can use a piece of equipment, or follow a practical procedure, that they have not previously met	
		Students are better at using a piece of equipment, or following a practical procedure, that they have previously met	
C By doing this activity, students should develop their understanding of the scientific approach to enquiry		Students have a better *general understanding* of scientific enquiry	
		Students have a better *understanding of some specific aspects* of scientific enquiry	

If you have ticked this box, please complete the table below

Specific aspects of scientific enquiry	Tick ✔ all that apply
How to identify a good investigation question	
How to plan a strategy for collecting data to address a question	
How to choose equipment for an investigation	
How to present data clearly	
How to analyse data to reveal or display patterns	
How to draw and present conclusions based on evidence	
How to assess how confident you can be that a conclusion is correct	

2 Design

2.1 How open/closed? (Tick ✔ one box)	
Question given, and detailed instructions on procedure	
Question given, and outline guidance on procedure; some choices left to students	
Question given, but students choose how to proceed	
Students decide the question and how to proceed	
2.2 Logical structure of the activity (Tick ✔ one box)	
Collect data on a situation, then think about how it might be summarised or explained	
Use current ideas to generate a question or prediction; collect data to explore or test	
Other. Please describe:	
2.3 Importance of scientific ideas (to carry out the activity well) (Rate: 4= essential; 3=fairly; 2=not very; 1=unimportant)	
Importance of an understanding of scientific ideas	
2.4 What students have to do with objects and materials (Tick ✔ all that apply)	
Use an observing or measuring instrument	
Follow a standard practical procedure	
Present or display an object or material	
Make an object	
Make a sample of a material or substance	
Make an event happen (produce a phenomenon)	
Observe an aspect or property of an object, material, or event	
Measure a quantity	
2.5 What students have to 'do' with ideas (Tick ✔ all that apply)	
Report observations using scientific terminology	
Identify a similarity or difference (between objects, or materials, or events)	
Explore the effect on an outcome of a specific change (e.g. of using a different object, or material, or procedure)	
Explore how an outcome variable changes with time	
Explore how an outcome variable changes when the value of a continuous independent variable changes	
Explore how an outcome variable changes when each of two (or more) independent variables changes	
Design a measurement or observation procedure	
Obtain a value of a derived quantity (i.e. one that cannot be directly measured)	
Make and/or test a prediction	
Decide if a given explanation applies to the particular situation observed	
Decide which of two (or more) given explanations best fits the data	
Suggest a possible explanation for data	

3 Presentation

3.1 How is the purpose, or rationale, communicated to students? (Tick ✔ one box)	
Activity is proposed by teacher; no explicit links made to previous work	
Purpose of activity explained by teacher, and explicitly linked to preceding work	
Teacher uses class discussion to help students see how the activity can help answer a question of interest	
Purpose of activity readily apparent to the students; clearly follows from previous work	
Activity is proposed and specified by the students, following discussion	
3.2 How is the activity explained to students? (Tick ✔ all that apply)	
Orally by the teacher	
Written instructions on OHP or data projector	
Worksheet	
(All or part of) procedure demonstrated by teacher beforehand	
3.3 Whole class discussion before the practical activity begins? (Tick ✔ all that apply)	
None	
About equipment and procedures to be used	
About ideas, concepts, theories, and models that are relevant to the activity	
About aspects of scientific enquiry that relate to the activity	
3.4 Whole class discussion following the practical activity? (Tick ✔ all that apply)	
None	
About confirming 'what we have seen'	
Centred around a demonstration in which the teacher repeats the practical activity	
About how to explain observations, and to develop conceptual ideas that relate to the task	
About aspects of investigation design, quality of data, confidence in conclusions, etc.	
3.5 Students' record of the activity (Tick ✔ one box)	
None	
Notes, as the student wishes	
A completed worksheet	
Written report with a given format	
Written report in a format chosen by the student	
Other. Please describe:	

4 Learning demand

In the light of your entries above, how would you judge the **learning demand** of this activity?

(Rate: 5=very high; 4=fairly high; 3=moderate; 2=fairly low; 1=very low)

Learning demand	

5 Assessment of effectiveness when used

A   Effectiveness at level (1)

Key question: Did students do what they were intended to do, and see what they were intended to see?

		Mainly yes	Mainly no	Not applicable
1	Did students know how to use the equipment involved?			
2	Were students able to set up the apparatus, and handle the materials involved, correctly and safely?			
3	Were students able to use the apparatus with sufficient precision to make the necessary observations or measurements?			
4	Were students able to carry out any routine procedures involved?			
5	Were students able to follow any oral or written instructions given?			
6	Did students observe the outcome(s) or effect(s) you wanted them to see?			
7	Could students explain the purpose of the activity if asked? (what they were doing it for)			
8	Did students talk about the activity using the scientific terms and ideas you would have wished them to use?			

B   Effectiveness at level (2)

Key question: Did students learn what they were intended to learn?

		Most	Some	Only a few
1	How many students could recall what they did, and the main features of what they observed?			
Summarise the evidence for your answer above:				

		Most	Some	Only a few
2	How many students have a better understanding of the ideas the activity was intended to help them understand?			
Summarise the evidence for your answer above:				

A checklist for analysing and comparing up to 10 practical activities

1 Learning objective(s) (or intended learning outcome(s))

Activity number →	1	2	3	4	5	6	7	8	9	10
1.1 Objective (in general terms) (Enter '1' for the **main objective**; '2' if necessary for a **subsidiary objective**.)										
A By doing this activity, students should develop their knowledge and understanding of the natural world										
B By doing this activity, students should learn how to use a piece of laboratory equipment or follow a standard practical procedure										
C By doing this activity, students should develop their understanding of the scientific approach to enquiry										
1.2 Learning objective (more specifically) (Tick ✔ **one** box in each group for which you have entered a number above).										
A1 Students can recall an observable feature of an object, or material, or event										
A2 Students can recall a 'pattern' in observations (e.g. a similarity, difference, trend, relationship)										
A3 Students have a better understanding of a scientific idea, or concept, or explanation, or model, or theory										
B1 Students can use a piece of equipment, or follow a practical procedure, that they have not previously met										
B2 Students are better at using a piece of equipment, or following a practical procedure, that they have previously met										
C1 Students have a better *general understanding* of scientific enquiry										
C2 Students have a better *understanding of some specific aspects* of scientific enquiry										

For C2, rather than simply ticking ✔ the box, enter letters to indicate the *specific aspects* being taught, as follows:

a	How to identify a good investigation question	e	How to analyse data to reveal or display patterns
b	How to plan a strategy for collecting data to address a question	f	How to draw and present conclusions based on evidence
c	How to choose equipment for an investigation	g	How to assess how confident you can be that a conclusion is correct
d	How to present data clearly		

2 Design

Activity number →	1	2	3	4	5	6	7	8	9	10
2.1 Degree of direction given (how open/closed?) (Tick ✔ one box)										
Question given, and detailed instructions on procedure										
Question given, and outline guidance on procedure; some choices left to students										
Question given, but students choose how to proceed										
Students decide the question and how to proceed										
2.2 Logical structure of the activity (Tick ✔ one box)										
Collect data on a situation, then think about how it might be summarised or explained										
Use current ideas to generate a question or prediction; collect data to explore or test										
Other										
2.3 Importance of an understanding of scientific ideas (to carry out the activity well) (Rate: 4= essential; 3=fairly; 2=not very; 1=unimportant)										
Importance of an understanding of scientific ideas										
2.4 What students have to do with objects and materials (Tick ✔ all that apply)										
Use an observing or measuring instrument										
Follow a standard practical procedure										
Present or display an object or material										
Make an object										
Make a sample of a material or substance										
Make an event happen (produce a phenomenon)										
Observe an aspect or property of an object, material, or event										
Measure a quantity										
2.5 What students have to 'do' with ideas (Tick ✔ all that apply)										
Report observations using scientific terminology										
Identify a similarity or difference (between objects, or materials, or events)										
Explore the effect on an outcome of a specific change (e.g. of using a different object, or material, or procedure)										
Explore how an outcome variable changes with time										
Explore how an outcome variable changes when the value of a continuous independent variable changes										
Explore how an outcome variable changes when each of two (or more) independent variables changes										
Design a measurement or observation procedure										
Obtain a value of a derived quantity (i.e. one that cannot be directly measured)										
Make and/or test a prediction										
Decide if a given explanation applies to the particular situation observed										
Decide which of two (or more) given explanations best fits the data										
Suggest a possible explanation for data										

3 Presentation

Activity number →	1	2	3	4	5	6	7	8	9	10
3.1 How is the purpose, or rationale, communicated to students? (Tick ✔ one box)										
Activity is proposed by teacher; no explicit links made to previous work										
Purpose of activity explained by teacher, and explicitly linked to preceding work										
Teacher uses class discussion to help students see how the activity can help answer a question of interest										
Purpose of activity readily apparent to the students; clearly follows from previous work										
Activity is proposed and specified by the students, following discussion										
3.2 How is the activity explained to students? (Tick ✔ all that apply)										
Orally by the teacher										
Written instructions on OHP or data projector Worksheet										
(All or part of) procedure demonstrated by teacher beforehand										
3.3 Whole class discussion before the practical activity begins? (Tick ✔ all that apply)										
None										
About equipment and procedures to be used										
About ideas, concepts, theories, and models that are relevant to the activity										
About aspects of scientific enquiry that relate to the activity										
3.4 Whole class discussion following the practical activity? (Tick ✔ all that apply)										
None										
About confirming 'what we have seen'										
Centred around a demonstration in which the teacher repeats the practical activity										
About how to explain observations, and to develop conceptual ideas that relate to the task										
About aspects of investigation design, quality of data, confidence in conclusions, etc.										
3.5 Students' record of the activity (Tick ✔ one box)										
None										
Notes, as the student wishes										
A completed worksheet										
Written report with a given format										
Written report in a format chosen by the student										
Other										

4   Learning demand

In the light of your entries above, how would you judge the **learning demand** of this activity?

(Rate: 5=very high; 4=fairly high; 3=moderate; 2=fairly low; 1=very low)

Learning demand										